Gold Stars®

Ready for School
Big Workbook

ball

PaRragon

Bath · New York · Cologne · Melbourne · Delhi
Hong Kong · Shenzhen · Singapore · Amsterdam

Helping your child

Remember that the activities in this book should be enjoyed by your child. Try to find a quiet place to work.

Always give your child lots of encouragement and praise.

Remember that the gold stars and badges are a reward for effort as well as for achievement.

Your child does not need to complete each page in one go. Always stop before your child grows tired, and come back to the same page another time.

It is important to work through the pages in the right order because the activities do get progressively more difficult.

The answers to the activities are on pages 124–128.

This edition published by Parragon Books Ltd in 2014

Parragon Books Ltd
Chartist House
15–17 Trim Street
Bath BA1 1HA, UK
www.parragon.com

Illustrated by Simon Abbott
Written by Betty Root
Educational consultants: Stephanie Cooper and Christine Vaughan

ISBN 978-1-4723-5681-9

Printed in China

Contents

Go together

Start at the red dot. Draw along each path.
Try not to touch the lines.

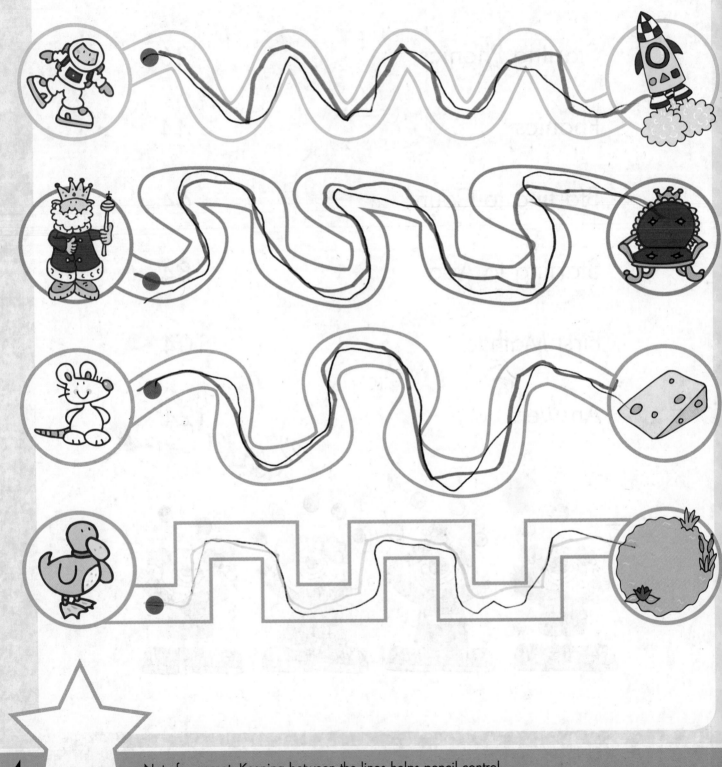

Note for parent: Keeping between the lines helps pencil control.

Curly tails

Join the dots to draw the tails on the animals, then colour them in.

Shadows

Draw lines to join each picture to its shadow.
Try to make straight lines.
The first one has been done for you.

Note for parent: This activity gives children practice in pencil control for straight and wiggly lines.

Big and little circles

Trace the circles, then the patterns inside them.

Note for parent: This activity gives children further practice in pencil control.

7

Straight and curvy lines

Draw over the dotted lines to finish the picture.

Note for parent: This activity helps children to use a pencil carefully to complete pictures.

Colour the picture.

Safari park

Draw circles and curvy lines to finish this picture, then colour it in.

Flying kites

Draw over the dotted lines, then colour the kites to match the T-shirts.

Note for parent: This gives children practice in controlling the direction of their pencil.

11

Motor mazes

Trace over the dotted lines to find out which car gets to the finish first.

Note for parent: This gives children practice in controlling the direction of their pencil.

Trace over each dotted letter.

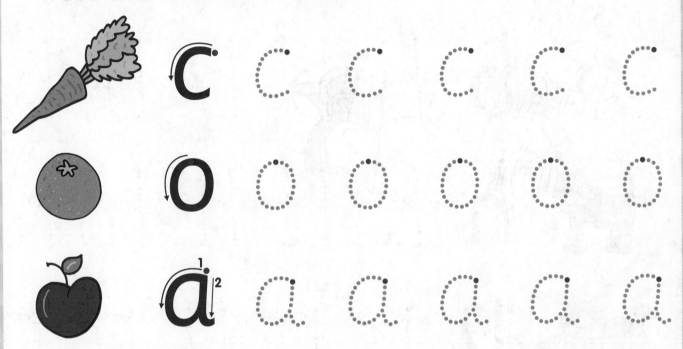

c c c c c c c
o o o o o o o
a a a a a a a

Trace the letters to finish these words.

orange

apple

carrot

Note for parent: These letters start in the same way, so it's helpful to see them together.

13

Trace over each dotted letter.

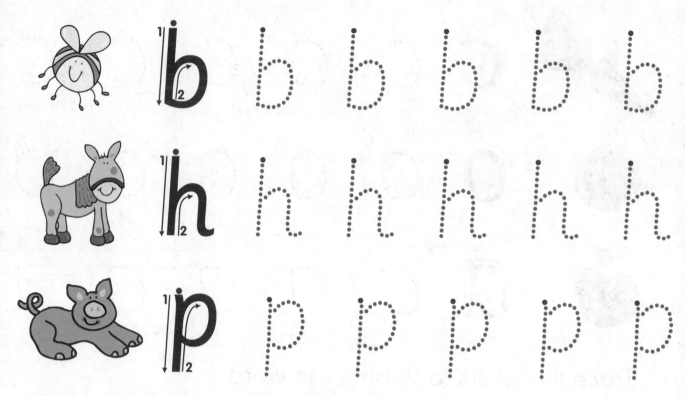

Trace the letters to finish these words.

bee

horse

pig

Note for parent: These letters start in the same way, so it's helpful to see them together.

Trace over each dotted letter.

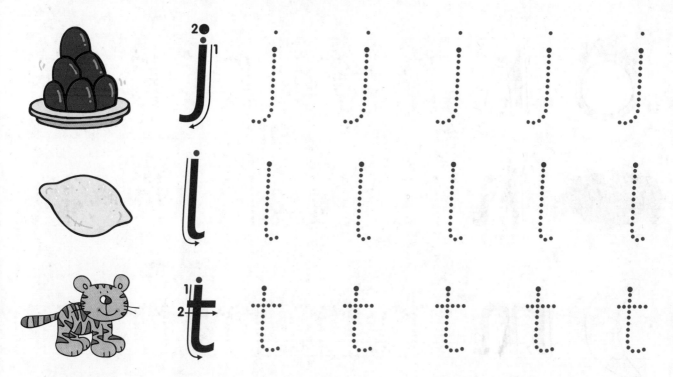

j j j j j j j j

i i i i i i i i

t t t t t t t t

Trace the letters to finish these words.

jelly

lemon

tiger

Trace over each dotted letter.

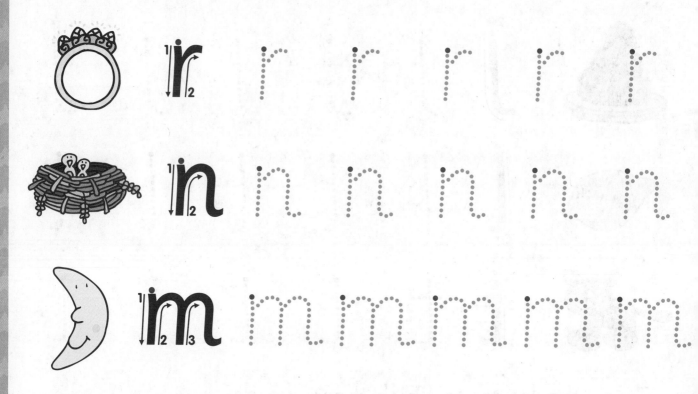

r r r r r r

n n n n n n

m m m m m m

Trace the letters to finish these words.

r ing

n est

m oon

Note for parent: These letters start in the same way, so it's helpful to see them together.

Trace over each dotted letter.

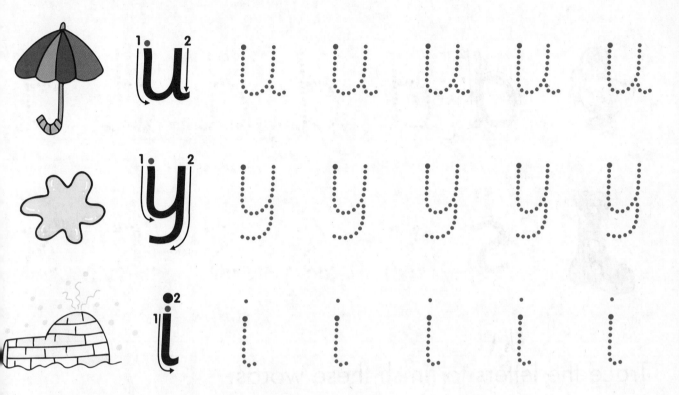

Trace the letters to finish these words.

mbrella

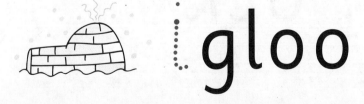

yellow

gloo

Trace over the dotted letters.

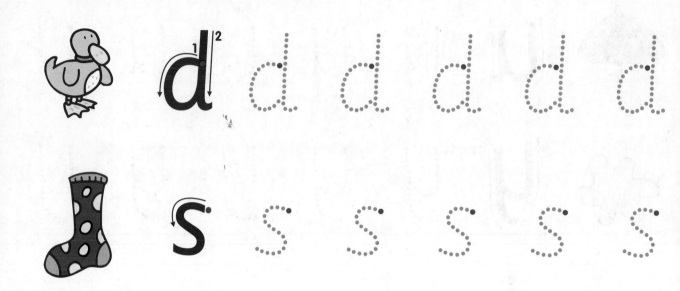

Trace the letters to finish these words.

duck

sock

Note for parent: These letters start in the same way, so it's helpful to see them together.

Trace over the dotted letters.

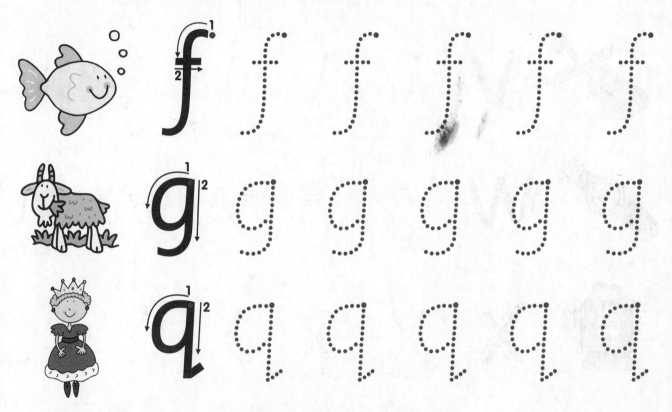

Trace the letters to finish these words.

fish

goat

queen

Trace over the dotted letters.

V v v v v v v v v

W w w w w w w w

X x x x x x x x

Trace the letters to finish these words.

violin

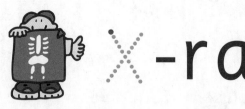
X-ray

watch

Note for parent: These letters start in the same way, so it's helpful to see them together.

Trace over the dotted letters.

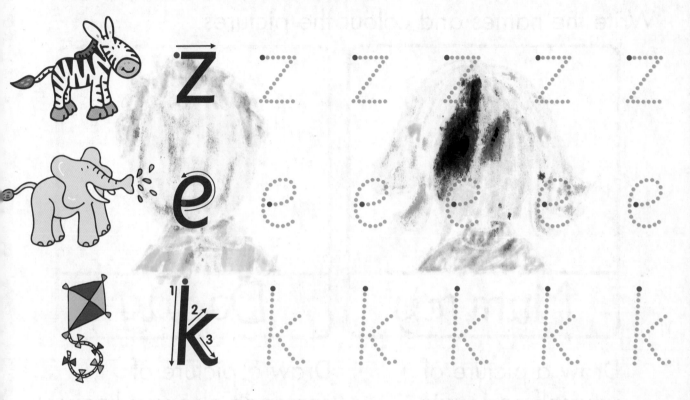

Trace the letters to finish these words.

zebra

elephant

kite

Writing names

All names begin with a capital letter.
Write the names and colour the pictures.

Mummy

Daddy

Draw a picture of yourself and write your name.

Draw a picture of someone else you know and write their name.

EVA

LOVEHEart

Note for parent: This activity helps children to learn that names begin with a capital letter.

Writing labels

Trace over the dotted letters to label each toy.

car

teddy

rocket

kite

yo-yo

ball

Trace each capital letter and write the matching small one beside it. The first one has been done for you.

A B C D E F G H I J K L M
a b c d e f g h i j k l m

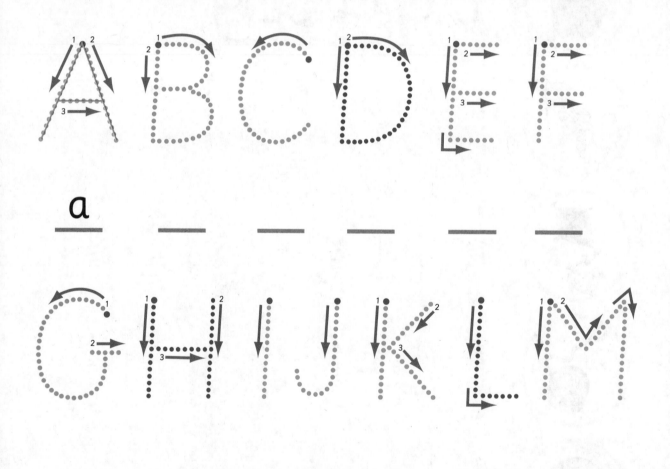

a

Note for parent: This activity helps children to recognize and write capital letters.

Write your name here, starting with a capital letter:

- -

N O P Q R S T U V W X Y Z
n o p q r s t u v w x y z

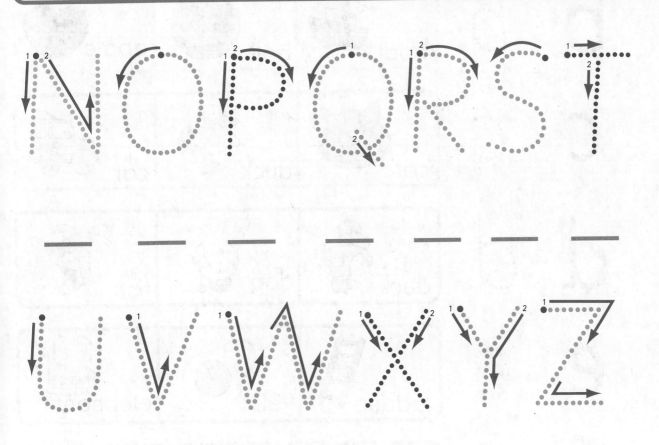

Write each letter, then circle the two things that start with that letter sound.

a   a

b   b

c   c

d   d

e   e

f   f

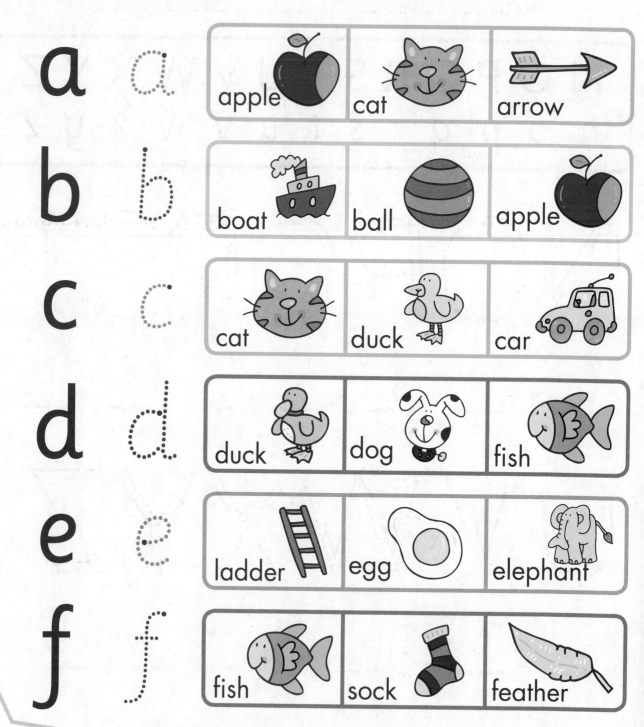

apple   cat   arrow

boat   ball   apple

cat   duck   car

duck   dog   fish

ladder   egg   elephant

fish   sock   feather

g

g

goat	gate	rocket

h

h

key	hand	helicopter

i

i

insect	lion	igloo

j

j

jar	juggler	ladybird

k

k

umbrella	key	king

l

l

ladder	car	lion

m

m

mouse	moon	hammer

Write each letter, then circle the two things that start with that letter sound.

n   n   n

o   o   o

p   p   p

q   q   q

r   r   r

s   s   s

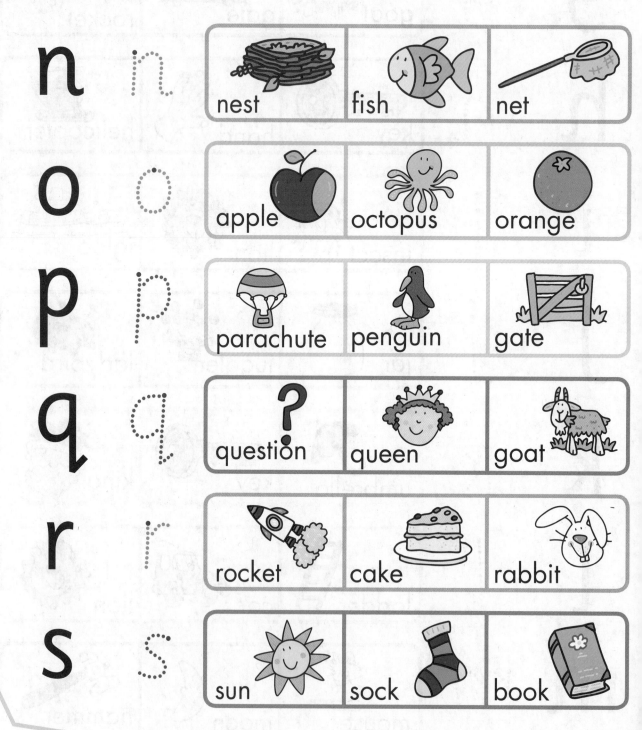

nest   fish   net

apple   octopus   orange

parachute   penguin   gate

question   queen   goat

rocket   cake   rabbit

sun   sock   book

Note for parent: This helps children to understand beginning sounds in words.

t
u
v
w
x
y
z

t
u
v
w
x
y
z

table lion teddy
umbrella fish umbrella
violin van bird
dog window watch
x-ray rabbit x-ray
yellow yo-yo sun
butterfly zip zebra

Read and find

Tick each thing when you spot it in the big picture.

dog ☐   **ball** ☐   **gate** ☐   **kite** ☐

cake ☐   **apple** ☐   **sun** ☐   **fox** ☐

Choose a letter sound

Look at each picture. Choose a letter and write it in the space to make each word.

m  p

__ an

t  r

__ at

s  p

__ ig

e 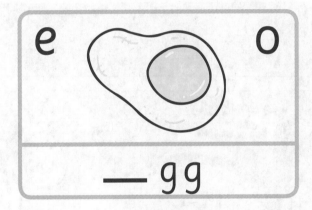 o

__ gg

b  z

__ ug

h 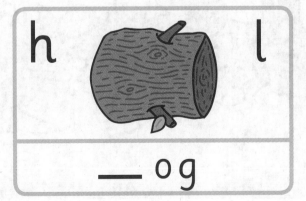 l

__ og

Note for parent: This gives children the opportunity to choose sounds and build words for themselves.

Read and find

Tick each thing when you spot it in the big picture.

zebra	☐	**bird**	☐	**window**	☐
tiger	☐	**nest**	☐	**baby kangaroo**	☐
vase	☐	**fox**	☐	**mummy kangaroo**	☐

Note for parent: This helps children start to read words and pictures together and to hear and see hard consonants at the beginning of words.

Choose a letter sound

Choose a letter to write at the start of each word.

f	h	t	b	k	z

_ish

_ird

_at

_ing

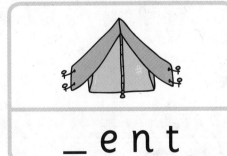

_ent

_ebra

Note for parent: This gives children the opportunity to choose and write hard consonant sounds and to build words.

33

Listen and match

Say the name of the picture in the middle of each group. Circle the things around it that begin with the same sound.

spoon

ladder

spade

spider

helicopter

spaghetti

cheese

whale

chick

chips

church

book

shark

king

shell

sheep

shoe

ambulance

Note for parent: As well as looking carefully at each word, encourage your child to say and listen to the sound at the start.

Making words

Choose and write the missing letter sound into each word.

f t x c f b l

_a_   _o_   _ee

o w_   _ish

Odd one out

Circle the odd one out in each group.

lion

kite

ladder

leaf

candle

cat

apple

comb

book

panda

pig

parachute

teddy

telephone

kite

table

Note for parent: This enables your child to read words and pictures and hear the difference
between initial sounds.

Plurals

Write a label for each picture. Add an **s** to the end because there is more than 1 thing.

hat   _ _ _ _

sock   _ _ _ _ _

bat   _ _ _ _

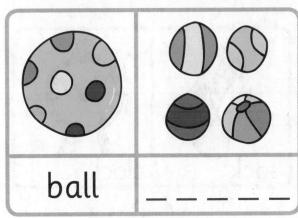

ball   _ _ _ _ _

tree   _ _ _ _ _

star   _ _ _ _ _

Note for parent: This activity helps children to learn how to write plurals.

Rhyming words

Do these words rhyme? Put a ✔ or a ✘ in the box under each pair of pictures.

house   mouse

car   boat

sock   clock

moon   star

key   tree

box   fox

Note for parent: Make sure you say these words out loud so your child can hear the words that rhyme.

Make the words

Write in the missing letter sounds to make the words.

| g n c w m b |

g_oat

rainbo_g

quee_m

dru_m

_cake

_book

Note for parent: This activity helps children to recognize the letters that make an individual word.

39

Sounds in the middle

Trace over these letters and say the sounds.

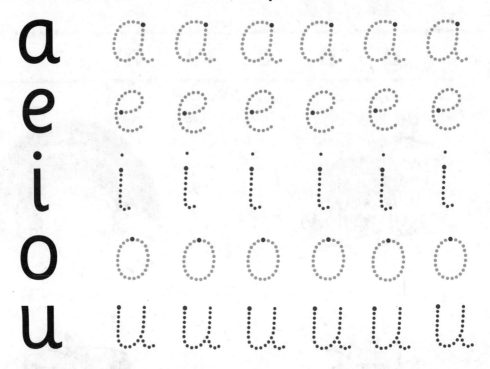

a a a a a a a a
e e e e e e e e
i i i i i i i i
o o o o o o o o
u u u u u u u u

Name each picture. Tick the words with an **a** sound in the middle.

Name each picture. Tick the words with an **e** sound in the middle.

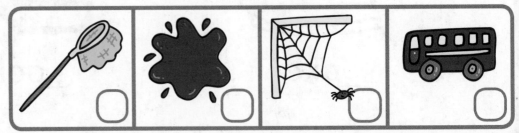

Note to parent: This activity helps children to identify the vowels a, e, i, o and u.

Name each picture. Tick the words with an **i** sound in the middle.

Name each picture. Tick the words with an **o** sound in the middle.

Name each picture. Tick the words with a **u** sound in the middle.

Make the sentences

Choose a word from this list to write into each sentence. Ask a grown-up to read each sentence out loud first.

and	**in**	**into**	**at**	**I**
he	**she**	**am**	**to**	**can**

The zebra looked __ the lion.

The fish jumped ____ the sea.

The cat ___ dog are friends.

Note for parent: This will help your child learn high frequency words that they will need to help them write and read independently.

The birds sat __ the nest.

"_ am the queen and __ is the king."

"I __ the king and ___ is the queen."

"I like __ eat grass."

"I ___ fly!"

Sounds the same

Draw lines to join the pictures that start in the same way. The first one has been done for you.

parrot

king

telephone

baby

kite

watch

butterfly

toothbrush

window

pineapple

Note for parent: This activity helps children to recognize the beginning sounds b, k, p, t and w.

Odd one out

Circle the odd word out in each row.

duck   ball   bee

panda   cat   pig

ring   hat   rainbow

cake   mouse   monkey

key   penguin   kite

Rhyming words

Read the word next to each picture.
Tick the 2 words that rhyme in each row.

chair

pear

box

flag

star

car

four

pear

door

star

eye

pie

bee

tree

four

Note to parent: This helps children hear word endings that sound the same, even though they are spelt differently.

Animal words

Choose a letter sound to write at the start of each animal word.

c d g r c p h

cow

horse

dog

pig

goat   rabbit   cat

What letter sounds do these begin with?
Write your answers.

 _ee    _at

Note for parent: This enables children to hear, read and write consonant sounds at the beginning of words.

Writing letters

Say the name of each picture and write its beginning letter.

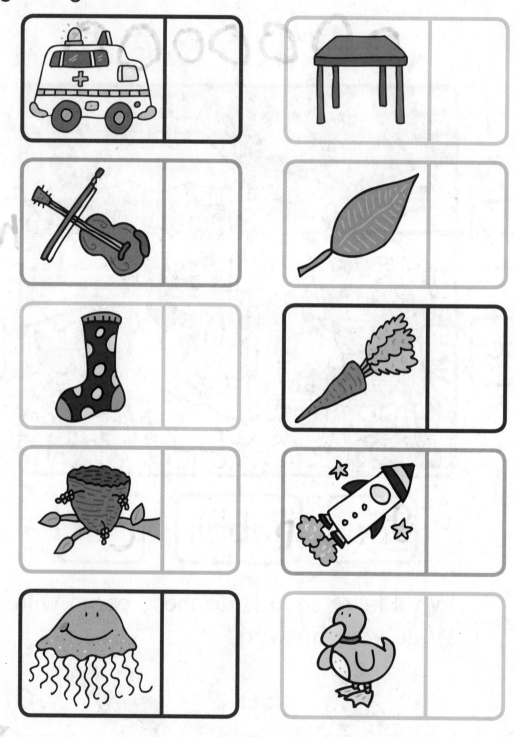

Note for parent: This activity gives practice in writing the letters a, c, d, j, l, n, r, s, t and v.

Find the rhymes

Colour the 6 pictures for the words that rhyme with Pat.

bat

cat

butterfly

cake

hat

Pat

egg

bat

rat

ball

mat

Now write a letter sound at the start of each word.

_ a t   _ a t   _ a t   _ a t

Note for parent: This gives children the opportunity to see, read and hear _at rhyming words as well as word-building practice.

49

Yes or no?

Write yes or no in each box: yes   no

fish   **begins with f?**

net   **begins with p?**

balloon   **begins with b?**

sun   **begins with s?**

umbrella   **begins with u?**

lighthouse   **begins with l?**

Note for parent: This enables children to recognize hard consonant sounds
at the start of words.

Use the letters from the box below to finish the words.

p n d g b w t n

c o __

t r a i __

m o __

p i __

c r a __

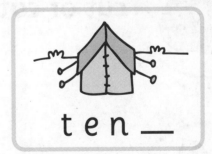

t e n __

s u __

b i r __

Note for parent: Word endings are difficult and need lots of practice.

51

Circle the word that goes with each picture.

 **dog or dig**

 **mup or mop**

 **hat or hot**

 **bas or bus**

 **cut or cat**

 **cup or cap**

 **pig or pog**

 **san or sun**

Note for parent: This will help your child gain confidence with simple consonant-vowel-consonant words.

Learn about th

Write over the **th** sound with your pencil.

th th th th th th

th th th th th th

Write the **th** sound at the beginning of these words.

_ _ u m b

_ _ i r t e e n

_ _ a n k s

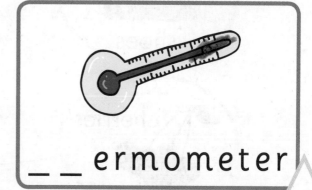

_ _ e r m o m e t e r

Note to parent: Your child will see the th sound in some high frequency words, like the, that, this, then and them.

53

ch and sh sounds

Draw lines to join 2 words that start with the same sound. There are 5 pairs altogether.

Note for parent: This activity helps your child learn about ch and sh.

Write **ch** or **sh** to finish the words.

 c̲h̲ _ a i r

 s̲h̲ e e p

 s̲h̲ o e s

 c̲h̲ u r c h

 c̲h̲ i c k

Crossword

Look at the pictures and spell the words to do the puzzle.

Note for parent: This will give your child confidence as they sound out and write consonant-vowel-consonant words.

Animals

Can you spot these animals in the big picture?

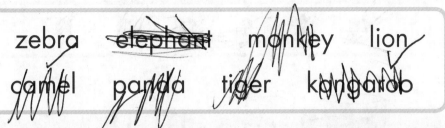

zebra ~~elephant~~ monkey lion ✓

camel panda tiger kangaroo

Which animal begins with z? Write it here.

Zebra

Which animal begins with l? Write it here.

 Lion

Note to parent: This activity helps children to identify the initial sounds c, e, k, l, m, p, t and z.

57

End sounds

Choose a sound to write at the end of each word.

g t s g p n

 m u _g_

 b u _s_

 d o _g_

 m a _p_

 n e _t_

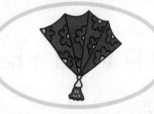 f a _n_

Note to parent: This gives children practice with the last consonant sound in words.

Say the word with each picture.
Look for each word in the grid.
Remember to look across and down.

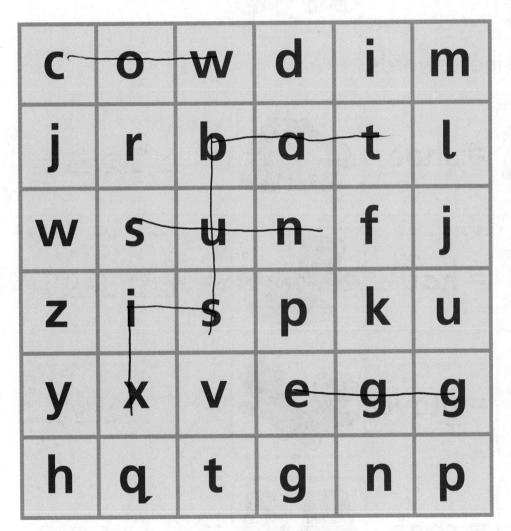

c	o	w	d	i	m
j	r	b	a	t	l
w	s	u	n	f	j
z	i	s	p	k	u
y	x	v	e	g	g
h	q	t	g	n	p

cow

bus

sun

egg

six **6**

bat

Note for parent: This is a chance to have fun looking for words.

59

s endings

You add the **s** sound to the end of a word when there is more than 1 thing.

 sock

 socks

Now write these words.

 = shoe

 = shoes

 = hat

 = hats

 = glove

 = gloves

 = coat

 = coats

Note for parent: This activity helps children to understand plurals.

Write **sh**, **ch** or **th** at the start of these words.

s h o e s

t h u m b

c h a i r

Write **sh**, **ch** or **th** at the end of these words.

t o o t h

w a t c h

b r u s h

Note for parent: This activity gives more practice with the double-letter sounds sh, ch and th.

61

Check the spelling

Look at the pictures and sound out the words.
Circle the word that goes with each picture.

ball
bell

hut
hat

fox
fos

pin
pen

cot
cat

man
men

Now write the word next to each picture.

p i g

s u n

Note to parent: This will help your child sound out consonant-vowel-consonant words and write them independently.

Picture quiz

Spot these things in the big picture.

~~bed~~   ~~mat~~   net

Now spot the thing that starts with **ch**.

Spot 3 things beginning with **b**.

Note to parent: This quiz is a quick revision of some of the sounds covered in the book.

63

Count one

Point to the number.
Trace it with your finger.

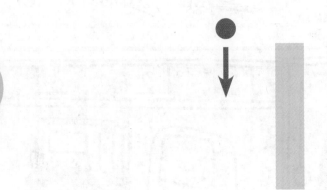

Point to each picture. Count how many and write the answer in each box.

Note for parent: Numbers are used to show position, to number the winners in a race for example, as well as to count 'how many?'.

How many candles can you count?

Who is number 1?
Write your answer on the dotted line.

Claire   Tim   Molly   ....

Draw one cherry
on the cake.

Point to the number.
Trace it with your finger.

Point to each picture.
Count how many and write the answer in each box.

Note for parent: Numbers are used to count 'how many?' and they are also used as labels, to number houses for example.

Circle the ladybird with two spots.

Who lives at house number 2?
Write the answer on the dotted line.

John   Emma   James   ....

Draw two candles
on the cake.

Count three

Point to the number.
Trace it with your finger.

Point to each picture. Count how many and write the answer in each box.

Note for parent: Before writing a number, your child should trace over the shape several times with their finger.

Circle the ball with three spots.

Circle bus number 3.

Draw three spots on the ladybird, then colour it in.

Point to the number.
Trace it with your finger.

Count how many candles. Draw a ring around the correct number. Now draw a ring around the correct number of horse's hooves.

1 2 3 4

1 2 3 4

Count the balloons.
Draw a ring around the teddy with four balloons.

Look at the picture. Tick the box for car number 4.

Point to the number.
Trace it with your finger.

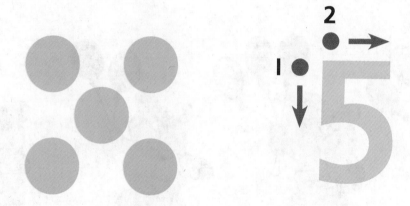

Look at the foot. Count how many toes and draw a ring around the correct number.

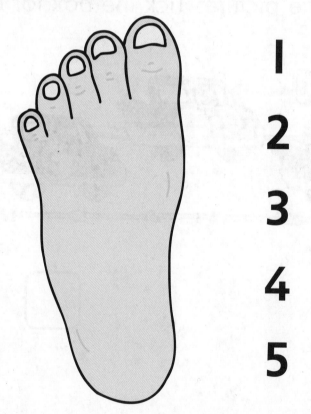

1
2
3
4
5

Note for parent: Encourage your child to use their fingers as they count.

Circle the clown with five balls.

Colour the dogs with five spots.

Draw five sausages in the pan.

Point to the number.
Trace it with your finger.

Count the bee's legs.
Draw a ring around
the correct number.

Count the hen's eggs. Write the number in the box.

Note for parent: Practise counting with real objects; move them around and ask if there are still the same number.

Look at the flowers. Colour the flower with six petals.

Colour six apples
in the tree.

Colour the bowl with six fish.

Count seven

Point to the number.
Trace it with your finger.

Count Snow White's dwarfs.
Count their beds.
Write the correct numbers in the boxes.

dwarfs ☐   beds ☐

Colour the group of seven presents.

Count eight

Point to the number.
Trace it with your finger.

Point to each sock. Count how many and write the answer in the box.

Count how many spider's legs and write the answer in the box.

Note for parent: When children count they need to co-ordinate saying the number whilst pointing to each object.

Colour eight butterflies.

Draw a line to join the rod
to duck number 8.

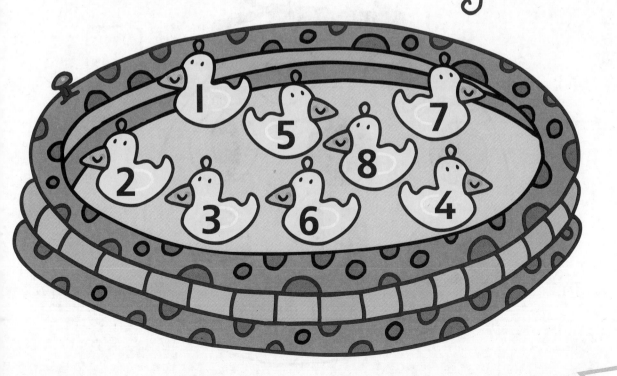

Note for parent: When your child can count confidently in ones, encourage them
to count in twos. Pairs of socks can help with this!

79

Count nine

Point to the number. Trace it with your finger.

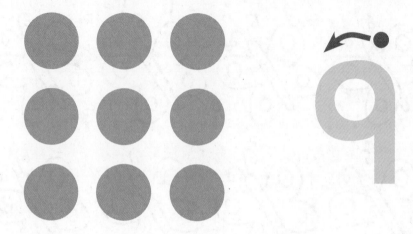

Count the marbles in the bag. Write the answer in the box.

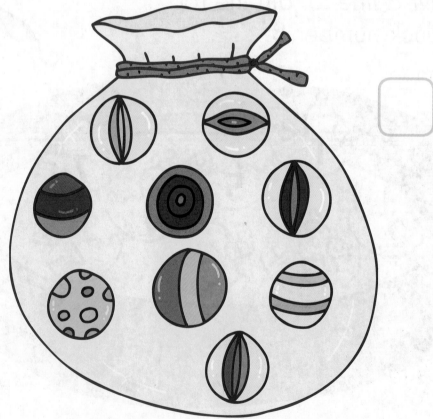

Note for parent: This activity gives your child practice in counting up to 9.

Colour nine fish in the pond.

Count the things in each set and write the answer in the box.

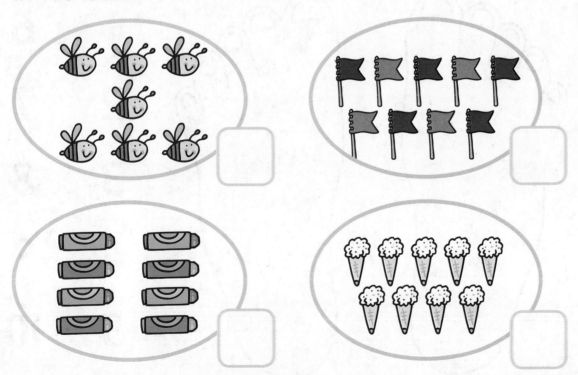

Note for parent: As your child begins to count everyday objects with confidence, encourage them to estimate the number of objects before they count.

81

Point to the number.
Trace it with your finger.

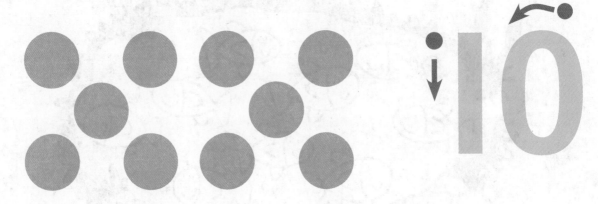

Look at the feet. Count how many toes and draw
a ring around the correct number.

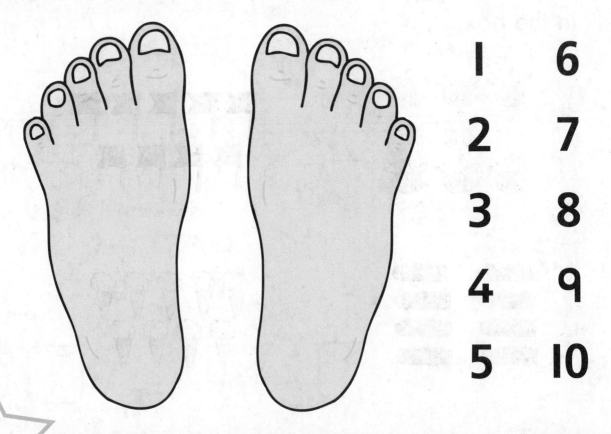

1	6
2	7
3	8
4	9
5	10

Note for parent: Also show your child how to count to 10 by using all the fingers on both hands.

Colour the snake with ten spots.

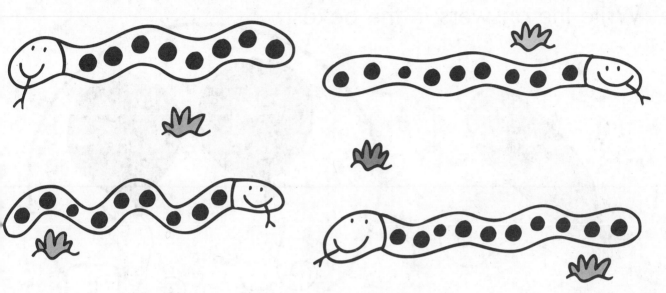

Colour the bottles on the wall. Count how many and draw a ring around the right number.

1 2 3 4 5 6 7 8 9 10

Count to 3

How many balloons can you count in each set?
Write the answers in the boxes.

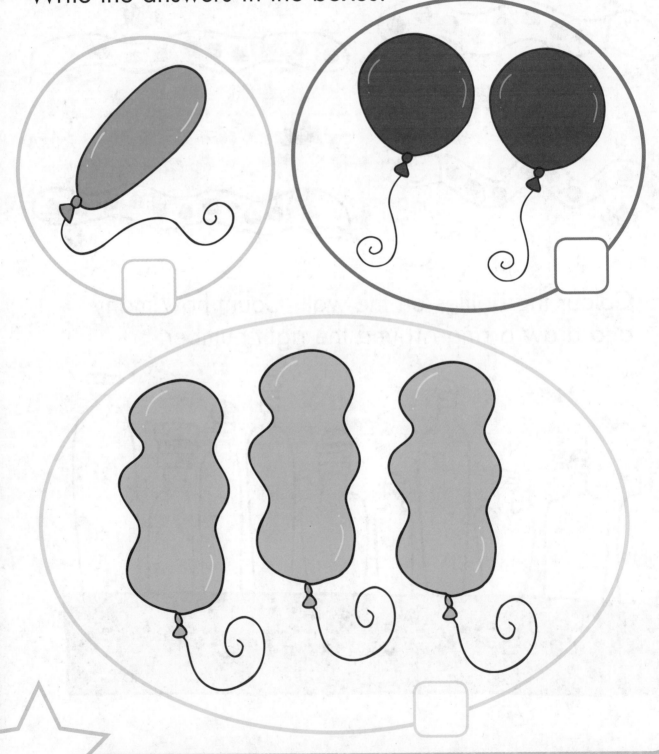

Note for parent: Children need to be confident with counting before they can start to add.

Count the spots on each shirt. Draw lines to join the T-shirts with the same number of spots.

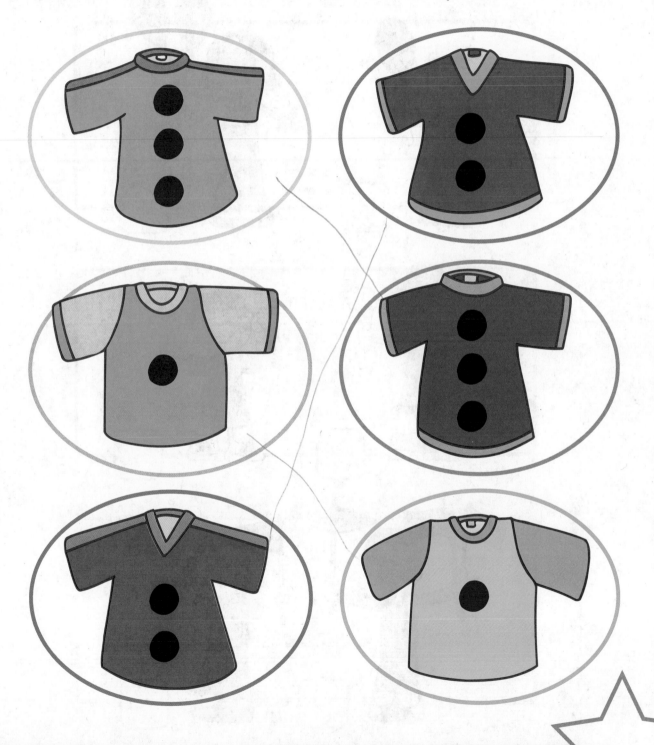

Note for parent: Identifying numbers that are the same or different prepares your child for adding and subtracting.

85

Who has more?

Look at the pictures. Put a tick by the person in each row who has more.

Note for parent: This activity gives more practice in counting from 1 to 3 and introduces the idea of 'more' and 'less'.

Another one

Each dog needs a ball. Draw 1 more.

Each child needs a cake. Draw 1 more.

Note for parent: Practise making numbers the same when you lay the table or share sweets.

One add one

Point to each picture and count the objects.
Say the numbers out loud.

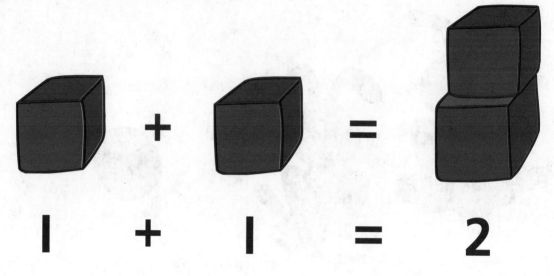

1 + 1 = 2

One and one make two.

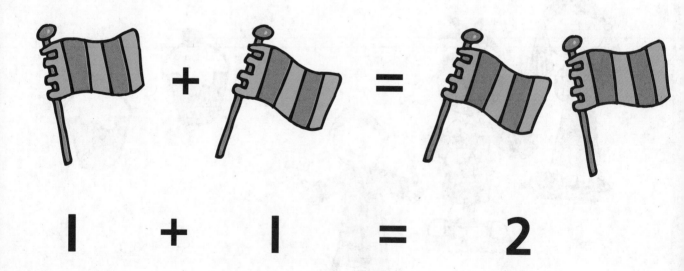

1 + 1 = 2

Note for parent: Follow the sums with your finger as you say them with your child.

Write the numbers in the boxes to make the totals.

1 + 1 =

1 + 1 =

Point to each picture and count the objects.
Say the numbers out loud.

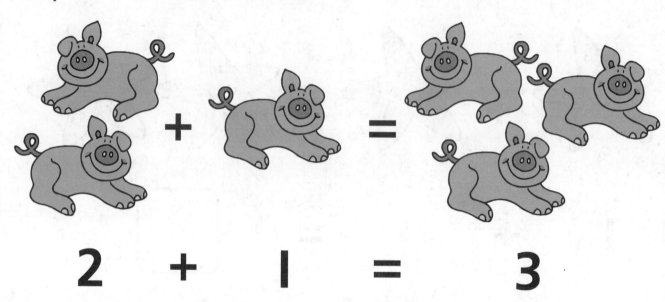

$$2 \quad + \quad 1 \quad = \quad 3$$

Two and one make three. Write the answer in the box.

$$2 \quad + \quad 1 \quad =$$

Colour the answers to these sums.

2 + 1 = 3

2 + 1 = 3

Colour four ducks.

Colour five fish.

Note for parent: Children often find it difficult to count objects that are not arranged in tidy rows: encourage them to cover up each one as they count it.

The same or more?

Join each rabbit to a hole. Are there more rabbits or holes? Tick the correct box.

more rabbits ☐   more holes ☐

Draw lines to see if there are more dogs or kennels. Tick the correct box.

more kennels ☐   more dogs ☐

Note for parent: Matching objects one by one shows if the numbers are the same or different.

93

Colour one more flag.

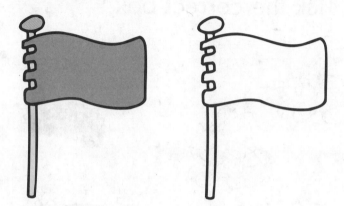

How many flags are there altogether?

Colour one more apple.

How many apples are there altogether?

94

Colour one more butterfly.

How many butterflies are there altogether?

Colour one more hat.

How many hats are there altogether?

Add 1

Point to each picture and count the objects.
Say the numbers out loud.

1   +   1   =   2

One and one make two.

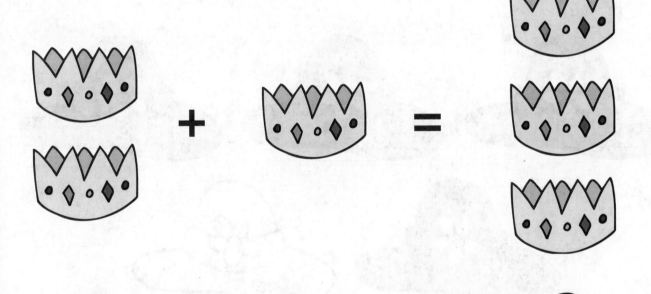

2   +   1   =   3

Note for parent: Count the objects in both pictures on the left with your child and point out that the last number in the count gives the total.

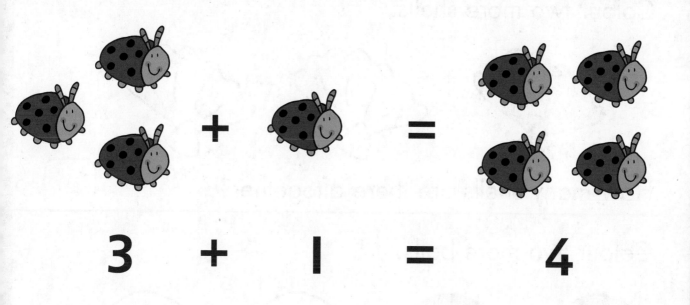

3 + 1 = 4

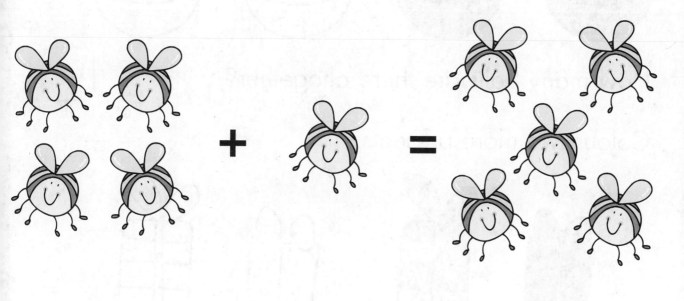

4 + 1 = 5

Two more

Colour two more shells.

How many shells are there altogether?

Colour two more balls.

How many balls are there altogether?

Colour two more presents.

How many presents are there altogether?

Note for parent: In this activity your child is adding things or objects in groups.

Add 2

Point to each picture and count the objects.
Say the numbers out loud.

1 + 2 = 3

One and two make three.

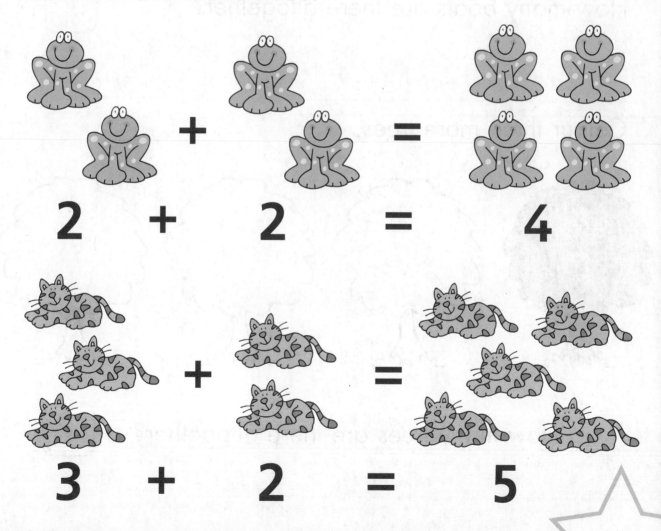

2 + 2 = 4

3 + 2 = 5

Note for parent: Practise counting groups of everyday objects (with totals of up to 5) with your child.

Colour three more boats.

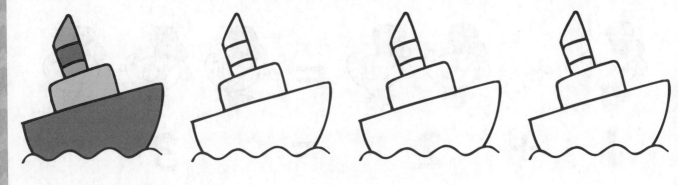

How many boats are there altogether?

Colour three more trees.

How many trees are there altogether?

Note for parent: Building brick towers is an excellent way to make number work fun.

Add 3

Point to each picture and count the objects.
Say the numbers out loud.

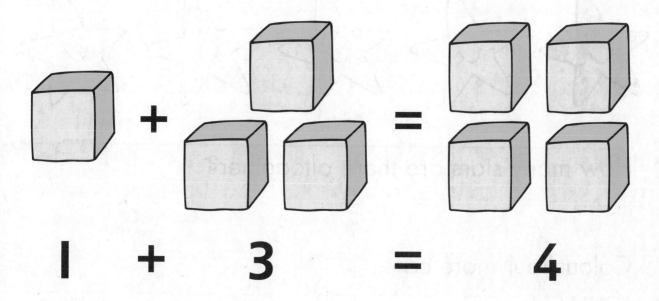

1 **+** **3** **=** **4**

One and three make four.

2 **+** **3** **=** **5**

Four more

Colour four more stars.

How many stars are there altogether?

Colour four more cars.

How many cars are there altogether?

Note for parent: Encourage your child to use their fingers to count and add.

Point to each picture and count the objects.
Say the numbers out loud.

| 1 | + | 4 | = | 5 |

One and four make five.

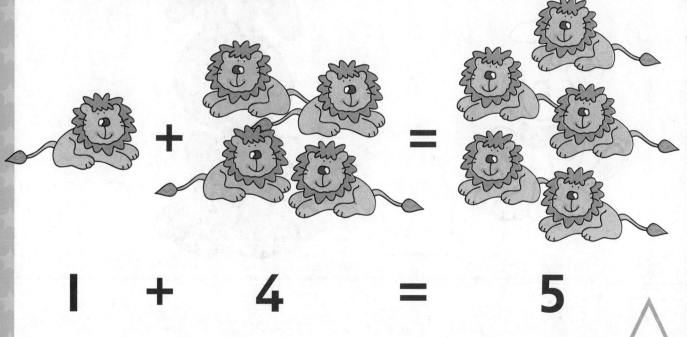

| 1 | + | 4 | = | 5 |

Big and little

Look at the pictures.
Put a tick by the things that are little.

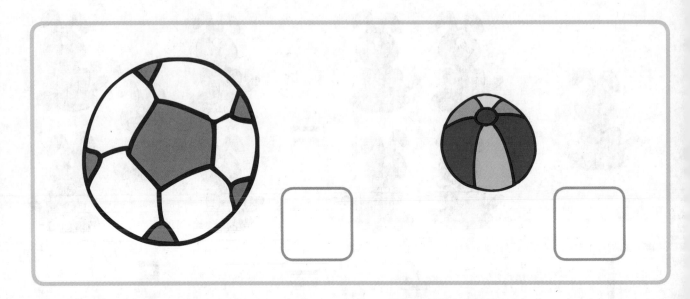

Circle the things that are big.

In, on, under

Can you see where the wolf is hiding?
Draw lines to join the pictures to the right words.

in	on	under

Draw a ball on the chair.

Draw a ball under
the table.

Draw a ball in the box.

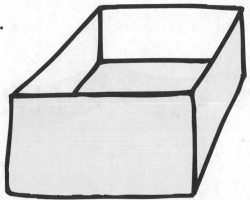

Long, short and tall

Trace the snakes with your finger.
Put a cross by the shortest snake. Say its colours.
Put a tick by the longest snake. Say its colours.

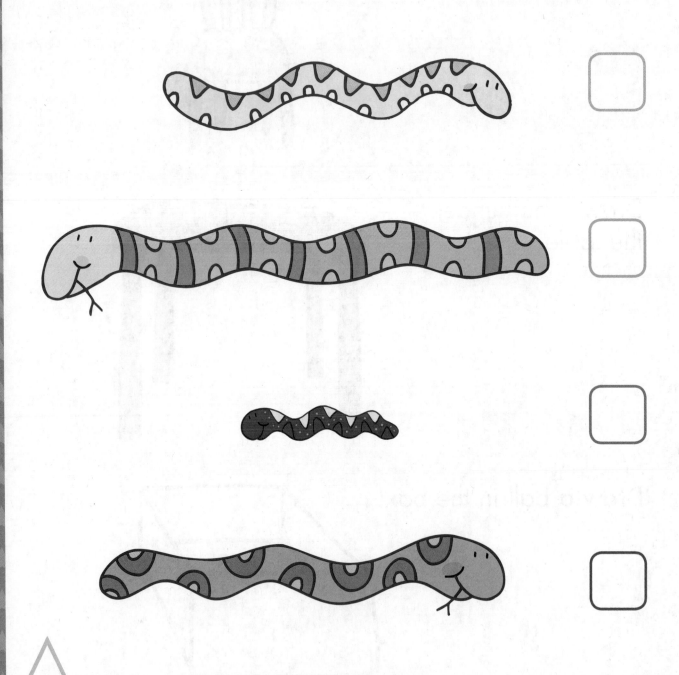

Note for parent: Length and height comparisons are the starting point for measurement. Practise comparing everyday objects. Ask your child which is bigger/smaller, heavier/lighter.

Look at the giraffes. Put a tick by the shortest giraffe. Put a cross by the tallest giraffe.

Draw lines to join each giraffe to its matching tree.

Heavy and light

Circle the things that are heavy.

Full or empty?

Look at the pictures. Circle the things that are empty.

Colour in some blue water in the empty bottle and in the empty bath to fill them.

Note for parent: Experiment with filling and emptying plastic containers at bath time.

111

Three bears

Draw lines to join each bear to the correct sized chair.

Draw lines to join each bear to the correct sized bowl.

Note for parent: Sequencing and matching are important number skills.
Ask your child to explain their decisions.

Draw lines to join each bear to the correct sized spoon.

Draw lines to join each bear to the correct sized bed.

Circles

Trace the circles with your finger.
Which circle is the smallest? Which circle is the biggest?

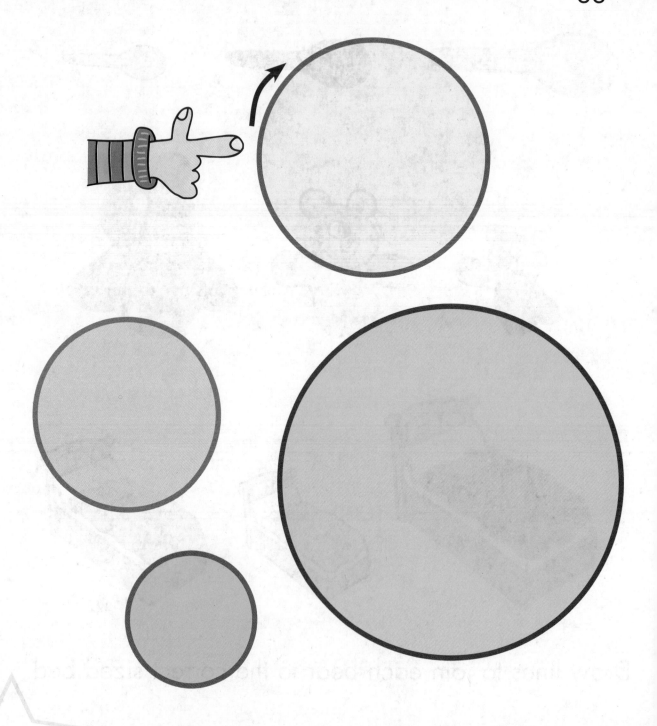

Note for parent: Even though they are different sizes and colours, all the circles are the same shape.

Look at the picture and find the circles.
Colour them in.

Triangles

Trace the triangle with your finger.

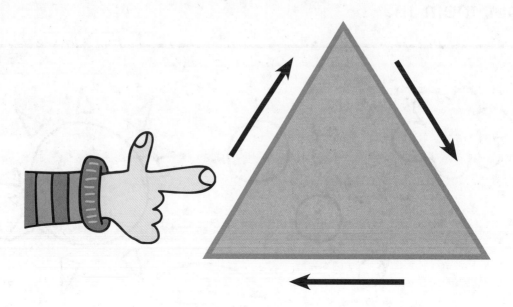

Count the sides – 1, 2, 3.
Trace over the dotted lines to complete each triangle.

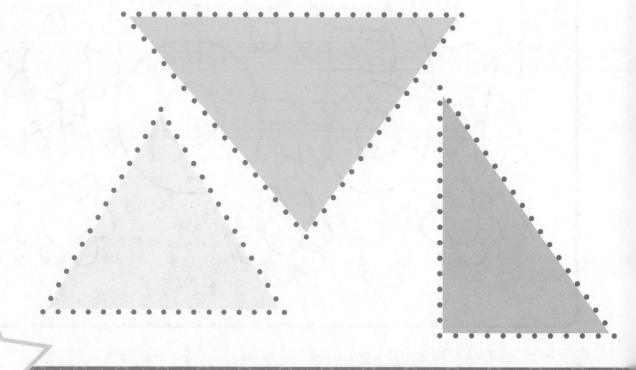

Note for parent: All triangles have three sides.

Look at the picture and find the triangles.
Colour them in.

Squares

Trace the square with your finger.
Count the sides – 1, 2, 3, 4.

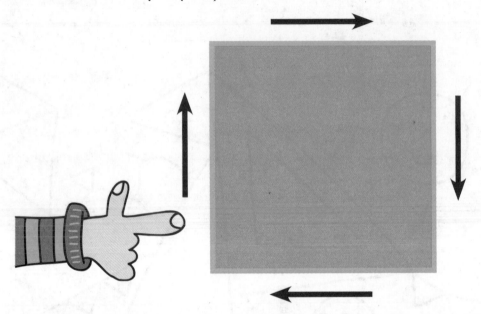

Trace over the dotted lines to finish the squares.
Colour the big square red.
Colour the small square blue.

Note for parent: Squares have four equal sides. Cut out some paper circles, triangles and squares and make pictures and patterns with your child.

Find the squares in this picture.
Colour them in.

Shapes and colours

Look at the pictures.
Name each shape and say its colour.

These shapes make 2 patterns.
Colour four more shapes to match the patterns.

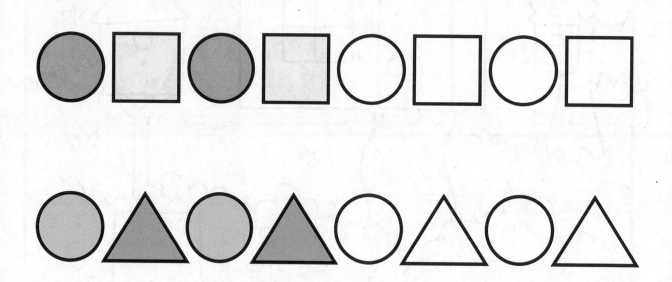

Note for parent: Knowing about colours and shapes helps children to sort and match.

Match the shapes

Join each object to its shape.

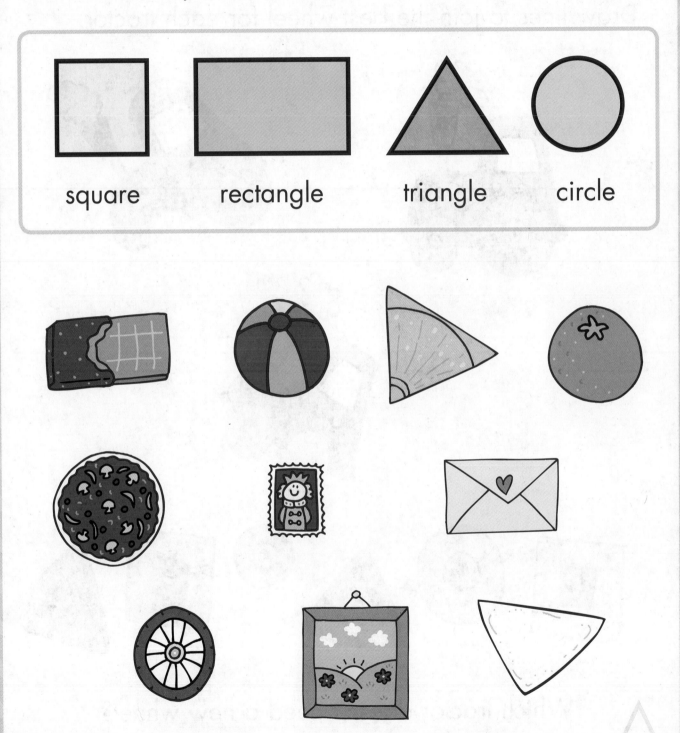

square   rectangle   triangle   circle

Note for parent: Practise shape recognition with your child by asking them to name the shapes of everyday objects. How are the objects similar? How are they different?

121

Shape fun

Two tractors need new wheels.
Draw lines to join the best wheel for each tractor.

Which tractor doesn't need a new wheel?

Note for parent: This activity gives further practice with shape and colour recognition.

Draw lines to join the lollies that are the same.

How many lollipops are circles?

How many lollipops are triangles?

Answers

Page 6

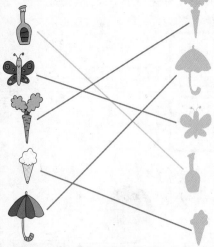

Page 11

Page 12

Pages 26–27

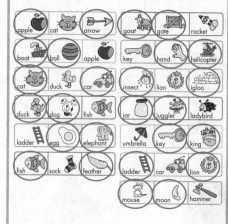

Pages 28–29

Page 30

Page 31

man, rat, pig, egg, bug, log.

Page 32

Page 33

fish, bird, hat, king, tent, zebra.

Page 34

spider: spaghetti, spoon, spade.
church: chick, cheese, chips.
sheep: shoe, shark, shell.

Page 35

cat, fox, bee, owl, fish.

Page 36

Page 37

hats, socks, bats, balls, trees, stars.

Page 38

Page 39

goat, rainbow, queen, drum, cake, book.

Pages 40–41

Pages 42–43

The zebra looked at the lion.
The fish jumped into the sea.
The cat and dog are friends.
The birds sat in the nest.
"I am the queen and he is the king."
"I am the king and she is the queen."
"I like to eat grass."
"I can fly!"

Page 44

parrot/pineapple,
telephone/toothbrush, kite/king,
butterfly/baby, window/watch.

Page 45

The odd ones out are: duck, cat, hat, cake, penguin.

Page 46

The words that rhyme are: chair/pear, star/car, four/door, eye/pie, bee/tree.

Page 47

bee, bat.

Page 48

ambulance, violin, sock, nest, jellyfish, table, leaf, carrot, rocket, duck.

Page 49

cat   mat   hat   bat   rat   bat
cat, rat, hat, bat.

Page 50

fish   begins with f?   yes
net   begins with p?   no
balloon begins with b?   yes
sun   begins with s?   yes
umbrella begins with u?   yes
lighthouse begins with l? yes

Page 51

cow, train, mop, pig, crab, tent, sun, bird.

Page 52

dog, mop, hat, bus, cat, cup, pig, sun.

Page 53

thumb, thirteen, thanks, thermometer.

Answers

Page 54

church/cheese, sheep/shell,
chick/chair, shoes/shark,
cherries/chocolate.

Page 55

chair, sheep, shoes, church, chick.

Page 56

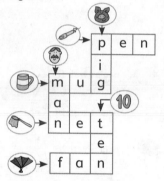

Page 57

zebra, lion.

Page 58

mug, bus, dog, map, net, fan.

Page 59

c	o	w	d	i	m
j	r	b	a	t	l
w	s	u	n	f	j
z	i	s	p	k	u
y	x	v	e	g	g
h	q	t	g	n	p

Page 60

shoes, hats, gloves, coats.

Page 61

shoes, thumb, chair.
tooth, watch, brush.

Page 62

bell, fox, cat, hat, pen, man.
pig, sun.

Page 63

chair begins with ch.
3 things beginning with b are bed,
book, basket.

Page 64

1 ball, 1 dog, 1 bone.

Page 65

1 candle
Tim is number 1.

Page 66

2 gloves, 2 shoes, 2 socks.

Page 67

Emma lives at number 2.

Page 68

3 bears, 3 chairs, 3 beds.

Page 69

Page 70

4 candles, 4 hooves.

Page 71

Page 72

There are 5 toes.

Page 73

Page 74

The bee has 6 legs.
The hen has 6 eggs.

Page 75

Page 76

There are 7 dwarfs.
There are 7 beds.

Page 77

Page 78

There are 8 socks.
The spider has 8 legs.

Page 79

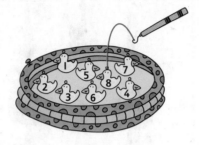

Page 80

There are 9 marbles.

Page 81

7 bees, 9 flags, 8 crayons,
9 ice creams.

Page 82

There are 10 toes.

Page 83

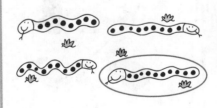

There are 10 bottles.

Page 84

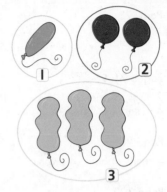

Page 85

Page 86

These people have more:

Page 89

1+1=2
1+1=2

Page 90

2+1=3

Page 93

more holes ✓   more dogs ✓

Pages 94–95

2 flags, 3 apples,
4 butterflies, 5 hats.

Page 98

3 shells, 4 balls, 4 presents.

Page 100

4 boats, 4 trees.

Page 102

5 stars, 5 cars.

Pages 104–105

Page 106

Page 108

The red snake is shortest.

The green snake is longest.

Page 109

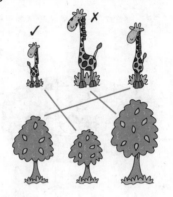

Page 110

The elephant and the tractor are heavy.

Page 111

Pages 112–113

Page 114

The smallest circle is green.
The biggest circle is blue.

Page 118

Page 120

yellow square, blue circle, green triangle.

Page 121

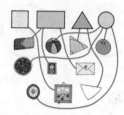

Page 122

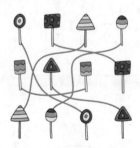

doesn't need
a new wheel.

Page 123

4 lollipops are circles.
4 lollipops are triangles.